Meet ... everyone from

JURASSIC PARK

Alan Grant knows a lot about dinosaurs. He works with **Ellie Sattler**.

John Hammond thinks that dinosaurs are great! He started Jurassic Park. He wants visitors to see the dinosaurs there.

Dennis Nedry works at Jurassic Park. He is very good with computers and he wants to be rich.

Lex and Tim are John Hammond's grandchildren. They want to see Jurassic Park. Lex loves computers and Tim loves dinosaurs.

Jurassic Park

Jurassic Park is in the Pacific Ocean. It is a theme park with dinosaurs!

T.rex

Raptor

Triceratops

Brachiosaurus

Before you read ...
What do you think? Are Lex and Tim going to like Jurassic Park?

New Words

What do these new words mean? Ask your teacher or use your dictionary.

fence

The animals are behind a **fence**.

DNA

I'm tall because it's in my **DNA**.

grandchildren

These are my **grandchildren**.

electric / electricity

This is an **electric** car. It stops when there is no **electricity**.

helicopter

Look at the **helicopter**!

lock

I'm **locking** it!

There are three **locks**.

money

This is **money**.

program

He is writing a computer **program**.

throw

He is **throwing** a ball.

visitors

There are a lot of **visitors**.

'What now?'

What now?

Verbs

Present	Past
break	broke
eat	ate
throw	threw

CHAPTER ONE
'Come to Jurassic Park!'

'Look! This was a raptor!' said Alan happily. He and Ellie loved finding old dinosaurs.

John Hammond came to see them.

'I love dinosaurs too!' he said. 'Come with me to Jurassic Park!'

At Jurassic Park, Alan and Ellie saw a very big dinosaur.

'Wow!' said Ellie. 'That's a Brachiosaurus!'

'But the Brachiosaurus lived a long time ago! How did you do this?' Alan asked John.

'Come and see!' John said. He opened the door to a small room.

'You have dinosaur DNA!' said Ellie.

'We find mosquitoes from the time of the dinosaurs,' said John. 'There's dinosaur DNA in the mosquitoes. We can make new dinosaurs with it.'

mosquito

'Look! This is a very young dinosaur,' said John happily. 'She's a Velociraptor.'

There were more raptors in Jurassic Park.

Alan was not happy. 'The raptors are beautiful,' he said. 'But they run very quickly and they can jump! You can't have visitors here.'

'It's OK,' answered John. 'We have tall electric fences.'

A man had a bag for Dennis Nedry.
'Is that my money?' asked Dennis.
'Shhh!' said the man.
'It's OK,' laughed Dennis. 'No one's listening.'
'We want the dinosaur DNA tomorrow,' the
man said quietly. 'Then you can have more money.'

CHAPTER TWO
'Something's coming!'

John Hammond's grandchildren came to the visitor centre at Jurassic Park.

'Today is going to be great!' said Tim. 'I love dinosaurs!'

'Do you like dinosaurs too?' Ellie asked Lex.

'No, she only likes computers!' said Tim.

The visitors went in two electric cars – one for Lex and Tim, and one for Alan and Ellie. They soon saw a Triceratops.

'Wow! She's big!' said Lex.

'She's very cool!' said Tim.

'But she can't walk,' said Ellie. 'I'm going to help her.'

Alan and the children went back to the cars, but Ellie stayed with the Triceratops.

In the computer room, Dennis started his new computer program. All the computers stopped and the lock on the DNA room opened. Dennis laughed happily.

Dennis went into the DNA room and came out with some dinosaur DNA. Then he ran to his car. 'I'm going to be rich!' he laughed.

There was no electricity in Jurassic Park because of Dennis's new program. The electric cars stopped.

'I think there's a problem,' said Tim.

THUD! THUD! THUD!

'Something's coming!' said Lex. 'And it's big!'
'It's OK,' said Tim. 'There's an electric fence.'
But the dinosaur broke the fence.
'Oh no!' shouted Tim. 'It's a T.rex!'

The T.rex ran to the children's car.

'Help!' the children shouted.

Alan ran out of his car with a light in his hand.

'Here!' he shouted, and he threw the light.

The T.rex saw the light and she ran after it.

'Come with me!' said Alan to the children quietly.

CHAPTER THREE
Hungry dinosaurs!

Alan walked with Lex and Tim.

'We're OK now,' he said.

They saw lots of small dinosaurs.

'Why are they running?' asked Tim.

Suddenly, the T.rex ate one of the dinosaurs.

'Run too!' shouted Alan.

John was frightened for his grandchildren.

'How can I help?' asked Ellie.

'You can start the electricity again – in the house next to the raptors,' he answered.

Ellie ran to the house and started the electricity. But behind her, the raptors were out in the park.

Dennis stopped his car. There was something on the road in front of him. It was a small dinosaur.

'Be nice to me, dinosaur!' he said.

But the dinosaur was hungry. She jumped on Dennis.

CHAPTER FOUR
Raptors!

Alan, Lex and Tim were back at the visitor centre.

'Wait here,' said Alan. 'I'm going to find Ellie.'

The children waited. But suddenly Tim saw something.

'Oh no! Raptors!' he shouted.

'Quick! Go to the kitchen!' said Lex.

'Stay very quiet!' said Tim.

The raptors walked slowly around the kitchen. One of the raptors saw Lex.

'Run!' shouted Tim.

The raptor jumped, but the children were quick. They ran away.

John Hammond saw them. 'Lex! Tim! Run to the computer room!' he shouted.

Everyone was in the computer room, but the raptors came after them.

'I can't lock the door!' said Alan.

'Oh no! It's because of Dennis and his computer program,' said John. 'Who's good with computers?'

'I am!' said Lex.

Lex worked at the computer.

'Be quick!' said Tim.

A raptor was at the door.

'She's very strong!' said Alan. 'I can't stop her!'

The raptor started to open the door. But Ellie helped Alan, and they closed it again. This time the door locked.

'You did it, Lex!' said Tim.

John shouted into his phone. 'We want a helicopter at Jurassic Park … and be quick!'

They all ran out of the visitor centre, but then they stopped. There was one raptor in front of them and a second behind them.

'What now?' asked Tim.

ROAR!

Suddenly the T.rex was there, and she was hungry. She ate one of the raptors.

'They're not looking at us!' said Tim. 'Let's run!'

Soon everyone was in the helicopter. The helicopter started to fly away. John looked down sadly at his dinosaurs.

In Jurassic Park, the T.rex was hungry again.

THE END

COOL DINOSAURS

The dinosaurs from Jurassic Park are beautiful and intelligent animals. How much do you know about them?

VELOCIRAPTOR (RAPTOR)

When: 115–108 million years ago

Food: meat, e.g. small dinosaurs

Did you know? Velociraptors sometimes stay in groups. A group of raptors can run after a big dinosaur.

TRICERATOPS

When: 68–66 million years ago

Food: plants

Did you know? This dinosaur is very strong. Triceratops also has three horns on its head.

HOW BIG WERE THE DINOSAURS?

1.88m

TYRANNOSAURUS REX (T.REX)

When: 68–66 million years ago

Food: meat, e.g. large dinosaurs like Triceratops

Did you know? The T.rex eats 140 kilograms of meat every day.

BRACHIOSAURUS

When: 154 million years ago

Food: plants

Did you know? You can hear the roar of Brachiosaurus from many kilometres away. It can eat plants up to 9 metres high.

★
What's your favourite dinosaur?
★

What do these words mean? Find out.
high   horn   intelligent
meat   plants

After you read

1 Match the names and the sentences.

a) John   i) She stopped the computer program.

b) Alan   ii) She helped a Triceratops.

c) Dennis iii) He ran to his car with the dinosaur DNA.

d) Lex   iv) He was frightened for his grandchildren.

e) Tim   v) He saw raptors in the visitor centre.

f) Ellie   vi) He threw a light for the T.rex.

2 True (✓) or False (✗)? Write in the box.

a) The T.rex broke an electric fence.   ✓

b) Lex loved dinosaurs.

c) The T.rex ran after Alan's light.

d) The raptors ate the T.rex.

e) A man had a bag with dinosaur DNA for Dennis.

Where's the popcorn?
Look in your book.
Can you find it?

Puzzle time!

1 Find five more words.

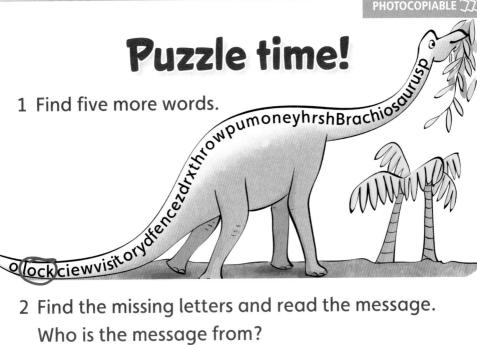

o (lock) ciewvisitorydfencezdrxthrowpumoneyhrshBrachiosaurusp

2 Find the missing letters and read the message.
Who is the message from?

There is a new ☐ ☐ **o** ☐ ☐ **m** on the

☐ **o m** ☐ **u t e** ☐ .

The ☐ **i** ☐ **o s** ☐ **u** ☐ **s** are breaking the

e l e ☐ **t** ☐ **i** ☐ fences.

Please help my ☐ ☐ ☐ ☐ ☐ **h i l** ☐ ☐ **e** ☐ !

🐾 = **a**   🐾 = **c**   🐾 = **d**   🐾 = **g**   🐾 = **n**   🐾 = **p**   🐾 = **r**

3 Look and match.

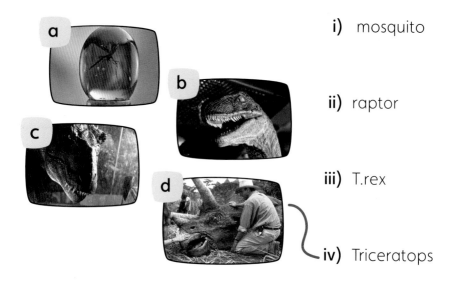

i) mosquito

ii) raptor

iii) T.rex

iv) Triceratops

4 Read and look. Which dinosaur is going to be at the fence first?

In one minute: the raptor can go four squares.

the T.rex can go three squares.

the Triceratops can go two squares.

the Brachiosaurus can go one square.

Imagine...

1 In small groups, choose a photo from the story.

2 Imagine you are in the photo. Can your friends guess the photo?

Chant

1  **Listen and read.**

The T.rex is coming!

The T.rex is coming!
I can hear her feet!
The T.rex is coming!
The T.rex wants to eat.
The T.rex is coming!
She isn't far away.
The T.rex is coming!
Run away!

The raptors are coming!
They're running! Oh no!
The raptors are coming!
Where can we go?
The raptors are coming!
Two or three or more.
The raptors are coming!
Lock the door!

2 **Say the chant.**